# SIDEWALK SPOOFING

How many things can you find wrong in this picture?

# WHOSE HAIR?

Who has hair like this? Put on your thinking wig and fill in the missing persons who grew these daring 'dos.

Illustrated by Lynn Adams

# HOORAY FOR H!

For each category below, see if you can name three things that begin with the letter "H."

## PARTS OF THE BODY

_____

_____

_____

## THINGS TO WEAR ON YOUR HEAD

_____

_____

_____

## SPORTS WORDS

_____

_____

_____

## ANIMALS WITH FOUR FEET

_____

_____

_____

Illustrated by Lisa Dayer

Answer on page 47.

# DREAM VACATION

Nikki loves to travel. She has made a list of places she wants to visit someday. Using her secret code, see if you can figure out the places she'd like to go on the vacation tour of her wildest dreams.

**My Code:**

| | | | | | | | |
|---|---|---|---|---|---|---|---|
| A = M | D = Y | G = O | J = Q | N = X | R = E | U = B | X = N |
| B = U | E = R | H = S | K = V | O = G | S = H | V = K | Y = D |
| C = W | F = T | I = Z | L = P | P = L | T = F | W = C | Z = I |
| | | | M = A | Q = J | | | |

PLACES TO GO

LPMWRH FG OG

1. AGGX
2. TEMXWR
3. KRXBH
4. MTEZWM
5. XRC QREHRD
6. MXFMEWFZWM
7. HMFBEX
8. KRXRIBRPM
9. FEMXHDPKMXZM
10. LRGEZM

Illustrated by John Nez

COME SEE!

ATLAS

Answer on page 47.

# CLOCK CLUB CLUES

Members of the Clock Club always take their time. They've left a message for new members to decipher. Using each hour from one o'clock to twelve o'clock only once, work through these clues to fill in the clocks with the correct hours. The last clock will tell you the hour for the next Clock Club meeting. The first one has been done for you.

1. Number of players on a baseball team

2. Number of scoops of ice cream in a double-dip cone

3. Number of months in a year

4. Number of singers in a trio

Illustrated by Terry Rogers

5. Number of seasons in a year

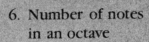
6. Number of notes
in an octave

7. Number of pilots on
a solo flight

8. Number of nickels
which equal a quarter

9. Number of legs
on an ant

10. Days in a week

11. Number of 100s
in 1,000

12. The club will be meeting
in the cafeteria at this hour

Answer on page 47.

# LET'S GO FOR A SPIN

The wheel on this page is filled with things that have wheels. Can you unscramble the groups of letters to find each item?

Answer on page 47.

1. O W N G G A R A U
2. M O I L B E A T U T
3. N R A I T
4. H A B E R W
5. R I L E A R T
6. C A
7. T L C R E C Y
8. B A D
9. S E G G Y U O R B A T O K
10. B P Y A
11. N E C E C
12. M O W I B L Y R E
13. L C M O T C O R O R E Y
14. O E L R S
15. C R A O R T
16. A G I C A R E T R T

Illustrated by Mike Ricketts

# WARM HOMECOMING

There's a big cup of hot chocolate waiting for this skier at the end of the trail. Can you find the path that will lead to it?

START

FINISH

# CREATURE FEATURE

These animals are confused. Can you help them
remember what they're really supposed to be doing?

1. If you were a dove, you might be:
   A) stewing B) cooing C) mewing.

2. If you were a parrot, you might be:
   A) gawking B) balking C) squawking.

3. If you were an eagle, you might be:
   A) soaring B) snoring C) pouring.

4. If you were a worm, you might be:
A) bawling B) hauling C) crawling.

5. If you were a sheep, you might be:
A) bleating B) cheating C) fleeting.

6. If you were an owl, you might be:
A) grunting B) hunting C) punting.

Answer on page 47.

# THIS ONE'S FOR THE BIRDS

These pictures are out of order. Can you number them to show what happened first, second, and so on?

Answer on page 47.

# POETIC PATHWAY

Hidden on this page is a familiar poem by Gelett Burgess about a funny-colored animal. See if you can discover the words. Start with "I" and move from left to right. Write down the words in each box where the answer to the arithmetic problem is two.

| 2 + 0<br>I | 3 + 3<br>always | 1 x 2<br>never | 2 + 1<br>wanted | 8 ÷ 4<br>saw |
|---|---|---|---|---|
| 6 − 4<br>a | 5 x 2<br>big | 11 − 3<br>blue | 4 + 0 − 2<br>purple | 1 + 6<br>moose |
| 8 ÷ 2<br>to | 4 ÷ 2<br>cow | 5 − 3<br>I | 9 − 5<br>carry | 4 + 4 − 3<br>home |
| 2 x 1<br>never | 3 + 2<br>my | 6 ÷ 2<br>books | 1 + 1<br>hope | 1 + 2 − 1<br>to |
| 0 + 6<br>leave | 1 + 1 + 2<br>and | 7 − 5<br>see | 3 + 4<br>me | 2 x 0<br>running |
| 20 ÷ 10<br>one | 8 + 1 − 6<br>two | 4 + 3 + 1<br>and | 8 − 4 ÷ 2<br>but | 3 x 1<br>when |
| 7 − 6 + 2<br>she | 5 + 3 ÷ 4<br>I | 3 x 3<br>because | 2 x 2 ÷ 2<br>can | 1 + 1<br>tell |
| 3 + 1 − 2<br>you | 9 ÷ 3 + 1<br>want | 6 + 4<br>dinner | 8 − 2<br>to | 18 ÷ 9<br>anyhow |
| 6 + 3 ÷ 3<br>go | 10 + 4 ÷ 7<br>I'd | 5 − 3 + 2<br>ski | 1 x 3 − 1<br>rather | 9 + 4 − 6<br>duck |
| 9 − 5 + 1<br>home | 14 ÷ 2 − 3<br>again | 8 + 2 ÷ 5<br>see | 6 x 2 − 8<br>somebody | 7 + 3 ÷ 2<br>juggle |
| 12 − 4 ÷ 4<br>than | 16 + 2 ÷ 6<br>wash | 14 + 2 − 6<br>clothes | 1 x 0 + 4<br>dog | 15 − 10 − 3<br>be |
| 0 x 4<br>alone | 1 x 10 ÷ 2<br>their | 7 − 5 x 3<br>happy | 9 x 1 + 4<br>feet | 6 + 4 ÷ 5<br>one! |

Answer on page 47.

# VA-VA-VA-VOOM!

A vast number of things whose names begin with V are visible on this page. How many can you verify?

Vinnie the Vundercat

SKI VERMONT

Victor

Vera

# LUNCH LOGIC

Use these clues to find out whose lunchbox is whose.

Kenny is saving his apple to eat after school.
Corinne will share her chips with Lee.
Lee will heat part of his lunch in the microwave.
Rieko is allergic to dairy products.

Answer on page 48.

# PICTURE CROSSWORD

These pictures will tell you what to write in the spaces across and down.

# SECRET SANDWICH

Kilroy has written the recipe for his
favorite kind of sandwich in his secret
code. Can you crack Kilroy's code?

**KILROY'S CODE:**

| | | |
|---|---|---|
| **A** = B | **K** = L | **U** = V |
| **B** = A | **L** = K | **V** = U |
| **C** = D | **M** = N | **W** = X |
| **D** = C | **N** = M | **X** = W |
| **E** = F | **O** = P | **Y** = Z |
| **F** = E | **P** = O | **Z** = Y |
| **G** = H | **Q** = R | |
| **H** = G | **R** = Q | |
| **I** = J | **S** = T | |
| **J** = I | **T** = S | |

TOQFBC B SGJDL KBZFQ PE OFBMVS AVSSFQ PM SXP

SPREAD A THICK
_____

OJFDFT PE XGPKF XGFBS SPBTS. OFFK B ABMBMB, TKJDF

_____

JS SGJMKZ, BMC TOQFBC SGF TKJDFT PUFQ SGF OFBMVS

_____

AVSSFQ. OVS SGF TBMCXJDG GBKUFT SPHFSGFQ BMC

_____

TFQUF JS PM B OBOFQ OKBSF.

_____

# ROW, ROW, ROW

Each clown has something in common with the two others in the same row. In the top row across, each clown has something with white polka dots. Look at the other rows across, down, and diagonally. Can you tell what's alike about each row of three?

Answer on page 48.

# PUZZLE PUZZLE

Can you find all the different types of puzzles hidden in the question mark? Look up, down, across, backward, and diagonally.

CODED MESSAGE
CRISSCROSS
CROSSWORD
CROSTIC
CRYPTOGRAM

DOT TO DOT
LOGIC
MATCHING
MATH
MAZE
MYSTERY MAP
PICTURES
QUIZ
RIDDLE

SCRAMBLED WORDS
WHAT'S WRONG
WORD SEARCH

```
      T O D O T T O D
    W H A T S W R O N G
    C W O R D S E A R C H O
    S C R A M B L E D W O R D S
    Z S W B E       O D D G L
    X I L O         E R N O
    A L U U         D O I G
    Z I S Q         M W H I
                    E S C C
                    Q S S T M
                    B U S O A Z
  M O X Q R I A R M
  E L D D I R G C
  L P Q U L O E
  S A S Q T
  S M O P
  O Y Y I
  R R C C
  C E I T
  S T T U
  S S S R
  I Y O E
  R M R S
  C I C S

        E E M H
        Z Z T I
        A A U U
        M T G Q
```

# BEACH BALL BONANZA

Sabrina's spending a sandy day at the seashore. She and her friends all brought different beach balls. Can you tell which beach ball is exactly the same size as Sabrina's? Which one is half as wide? Which one is twice as wide?

Illustrated by Terry Burton

# HARD TO PIN DOWN

The riddles on this page are all about pins. Can you name the kind of pin each one describes?

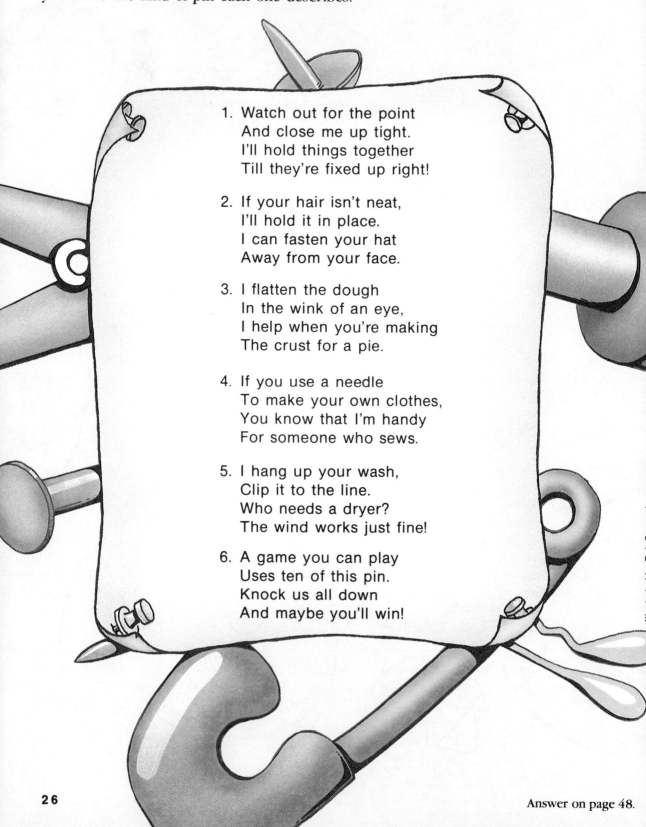

1. Watch out for the point
   And close me up tight.
   I'll hold things together
   Till they're fixed up right!

2. If your hair isn't neat,
   I'll hold it in place.
   I can fasten your hat
   Away from your face.

3. I flatten the dough
   In the wink of an eye,
   I help when you're making
   The crust for a pie.

4. If you use a needle
   To make your own clothes,
   You know that I'm handy
   For someone who sews.

5. I hang up your wash,
   Clip it to the line.
   Who needs a dryer?
   The wind works just fine!

6. A game you can play
   Uses ten of this pin.
   Knock us all down
   And maybe you'll win!

Answer on page 48.

# UNDERWATER MEMORIES

Take a long look at this picture. Try to remember everything
you see in it. Then turn the page, and try to answer some
questions about it without looking back.

Illustrated by John Nez

DON'T READ THIS UNTIL YOU HAVE LOOKED AT "Underwater Memories—Part 1" ON PAGE 27.

# UNDERWATER MEMORIES     Part 2

Can you answer these questions about the underwater scene you saw? Don't peek!

1. How many divers are in the picture?
2. What color is the deck chair?
3. Did the diver have two oxygen tanks or one?
4. What color is the coral the diver is holding?
5. What animal is on top of the wreck?
6. Are the ship's sails unfurled?
7. What is the clam holding?
8. What is the lobster doing?
9. What animal is "steering" the ship?
10. How many portholes are visible on the sunken ship?

Answer on page 48.

# MARY WHO?

There are lots of people named Mary, but there is only one Mary Poppins. See if you can match ten more first names with their storybook endings.

| | | |
|---|---|---|
| 1. Alice | A. Sawyer | |
| 2. Hans | B. Krupnik | |
| 3. Pippi | C. The Pooh | |
| 4. Tom | D. Crusoe | |
| 5. Winnie | E. In Wonderland | |
| 6. Peter | F. Brinker | |
| 7. Rebecca | G. Bedelia | |
| 8. Robinson | H. Of Sunnybrook Farm | |
| 9. Amelia | I. Longstocking | |
| 10. Anastasia | J. Pan | |

Answer on page 49.

Illustrated by Judith Hunt

# INSTANT PICTURE

What's hidden on this page? To find out, fill in every section that contains exactly two dots.

# CLEAN AS A SHELWIT

SHELWIT is the word WHISTLE scrambled. See if you can unscramble the other mixed-up words in this poem.

Cleaning my OMOR is my favorite RECHO.
As soon as I'm SNIFHIDE, I clean it some more.

I TYPEM the wastebasket three times and ENTH
I plump up my WILLOP again and again.

I pick up my clothes every night, every YAD.
I vacuum and SPEWE till the rug wears away.

I straighten my bookshelves first now and then ERLAT.
The SKOBO are so straight, they can't get any straighter.

I SHLIPO my desk so it sparkles and NEHISS.
My toys and my EGSAM stand like soldiers in lines.

You won't find a BEBCOW, no smudge from a hand,
I catch every dust speck FREEBO it can DLAN.

My room is so tidy and perfectly ATEN.
If you had no plate, off the ROLOF you could eat.

But mom's still not PHYAP, for I must confess . . .
My room may be clean, but my LESCOT'S a SEMS!

Answer on page 49.

Illustrated by Lynn Adams

# HOW LITTLE DO YOU KNOW?

Each of the people, places, and things in this quiz has the word "little" as part of its name. How many can you identify? If you know all ten, give yourself a BIG hand!

1. She had trouble keeping track of her sheep.

2. This city is the capital of Arkansas.

3. He took a nap under a haystack after blowing his horn.

4. This bird thought the sky was falling.

5. This friend of Robin Hood wasn't little at all.

6. She wouldn't eat with a spider nearby.

7. Leprechauns are also called this.

8. General Custer's last battle took place here.

9. The constellation Ursa Minor has another name.

10. This is a U.S. base in Antarctica.

Answer on page 49.

Illustrated by John Nez

# THE LONG AND THE SHORT OF IT

Four friends planned to meet at the boathouse. Each one took a different path. Whose path was the shortest? Whose was the longest?

Claire

Raoul

Devon

Gina

BOATHOUSE

FINISH

Answer on page 49.

# HIDDEN PICTURES

There are at least twenty-one objects hidden in this picture. How many can you find?

# MYSTERY MUNCHIES

Here is some unusual information about some very ordinary foods. Try to solve each mystery using the fewest numbered clues. If you still need help, the titles will give you the answer, but you'll have to unscramble them.

## A. CIE MAREC

1. It was first eaten by the ancient Chinese.
2. Marco Polo brought it from China to Europe in the thirteenth century.
3. It became popular in America in the 1800s because it was President Thomas Jefferson's favorite dessert.
4. A vendor at the 1904 World's Fair was selling this but ran out of dishes. The pastry vendor next door rolled up a wafer and put it inside.
5. Americans buy more than five million bars of this a year.

## B. GHSRARUMEB

1. These were first eaten in 13 A.D. by the Mongol Tartars. Their version was made of raw, shredded goat meat, camel meat, or horsemeat.
2. In 1921, the first major chain of restaurants to sell these started. They cost a nickel each and were shaped into thin squares.
3. If you buy one of these in Europe or Japan today, it will probably contain pork and maybe even rabbit meat or horsemeat.
4. The Germans in the city of Hamburg called them "beefsteaks." Americans call them something else.

## C. ONORPCP

1. It's about 5,600 years old.
2. The Pilgrims tasted this at the first Thanksgiving.
3. Colonial cooks served it with sugar and cream for breakfast.
4. It's in a tight waterproof shell. . . until it explodes!
5. Americans eat an average of forty-two quarts a year each.

## D. ZAPZI

1. This was invented over five hundred years ago by the women of Naples, Italy.
2. The first "fancy" one was created in 1889 for the queen of Italy, with ingredients that matched the color of the Italian flag.
3. American soldiers popularized this after World War II, when they returned to the U.S. from Italy.
4. Makers of this started to spin and flip it high into the air during the 1930s.
5. It means "pie" in Italian.

## E. OELCCTOHA

1. The Mayas and Aztecs were the first people to taste this.
2. The beans were once used as money in South America.
3. There are stories that the Aztec emperor, Montezuma II, drank fifty cups of this each day.
4. Americans eat about 2.4 billion pounds of this a year.

Answer on page 49.

Illustrated by Anni Matsick

# PICTURE MIXER

Copy these mixed-up squares in the spaces on the next page to put this picture back together. The letters and numbers tell you where each square belongs. The first one, A-3, has been done for you.

Illustrated by Rob Sepana

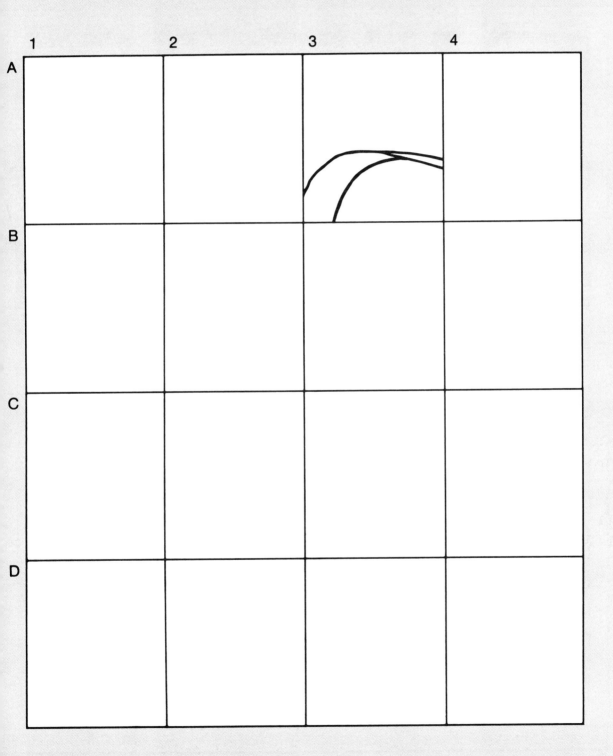

# TOY TOTALS

Take a look at Stephanie and Amanda's toy chest. How many circles can you find? How many triangles?

# DOT MAGIC

Connect the dots to make a picture of a popular singer.

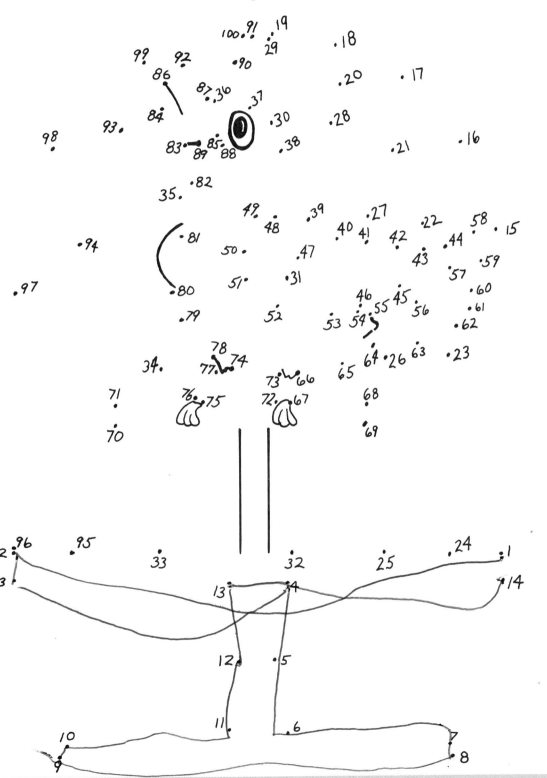

# CROSSWORD CROSSINGS

## ACROSS

1. Not new
4. Boston — Party
6. Hot — balloon
8. Polka —
9. Patricia's nickname
11. Female deer
12. Rock and roll, Bach, jazz, soul
14. What nonstop and none share
15. Little Tommy Tucker — for his supper
17. Tic — toe
18. Stitch
20. Cloudy mist along the ground
21. Nickname for Timothy
23. Sunbeam
24. Webbed wall on a tennis court

## DOWN

2. Do, re, mi, fa, sol, —
3. Go swimming, take a —
4. Part of your foot with a nail
5. Extraterrestrial
7. Male sheep
8. 'What's up, —?"
10. Ancient Greek or Roman garment
11. Rhymes with "rings" and means the same
13. Prince Charming is Queen Charming's —
15. Droop
16. — the table for dinner
17. Something to play with
19. Not lose
20. After mi and before sol
22. —, myself, and I

Illustrated by Anni Matsick

Answer on page 50.

# TRIPLE TROUBLE

Three children in one neighborhood are all celebrating their third birthday. Untangle the ribbons to see which present belongs to which child.

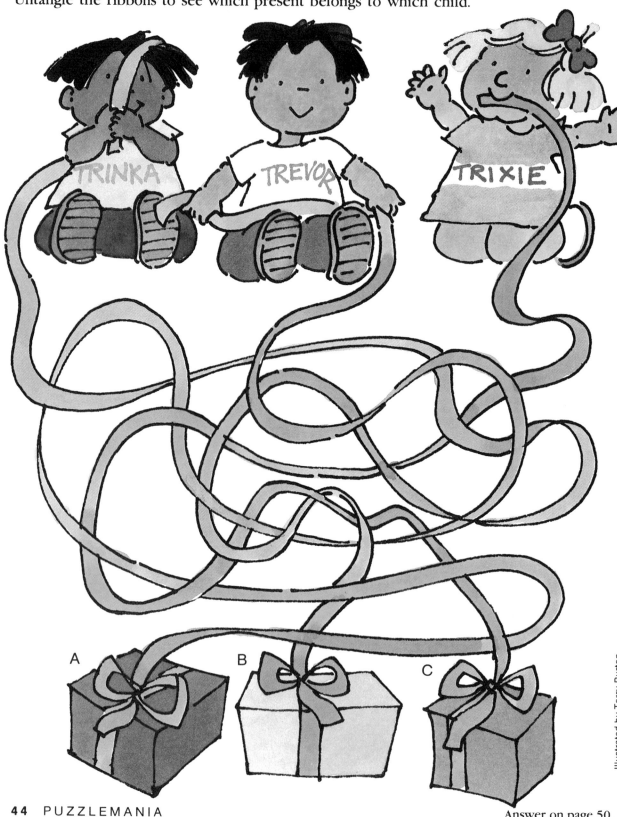

Answer on page 50.

Illustrated by Terry Burton

# WHAT'S IN A WORD?

There are at least thirty words that can be made out of the letters in DINOSAUR. How many can you find?

Answer on page 50.

Illustrated by Terry Rogers

# ZZZAP!

The letter Z may remind you of a buzzing bee or a snoring sleeper. It is found in dozens of words, some of which are listed here. See if you can find the words hidden in the letters below. Look up, down, across, backward, and diagonally. After you find them all, you should be able to zero in on five leftover Z's.

| | | | | | |
|---|---|---|---|---|---|
| AZALEA | DOZE | HAZY | PIZZA | WHEEZE | ZIGZAG |
| BREEZE | FEZ | HORIZON | PLAZA | WIZARD | ZING |
| BUZZARD | FREEZE | JAZZ | PUZZLE | ZEAL | ZIP |
| CZAR | GAZE | MAIZE | QUARTZ | ZEBRA | ZONE |
| DAZE | GRIZZLY | MAZE | SIZE | ZERO | ZOO |

The word search grid:

```
Z O O H F Z D Z S W
I W I Z A R D O I H
N Z P M A Z E N Z E
G R I Z Z L Y E E E
Q A Z M A I Z E Z Z
P U Z Z L E G A P E
B F A E E J D Z L Z
Z E B R A A C Z A R
I Z B O T Z L Z Z G
P H O R I Z O N A Z
```

Answer on page 50.

# ANSWERS

**OVER**

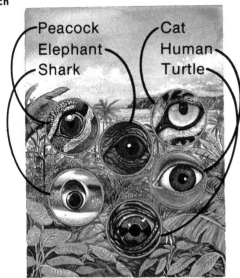

Peacock — Cat
Elephant — Human
Shark — Turtle

**HOORAY FOR HI** (page 6)

There are many good answers to this puzzle. Here is one set of answers that works. You may have found others.

**Parts of the Body**
hip
hand
heart

**Things to Wear on Your Head**
hat
helmet
hood

**Sports Words**
home run
halfback
hockey

**Animals with Four Feet**
horse
hamster
hippopotamus

**DREAM VACATION** (page 7)

PLACES TO GO

| | |
|---|---|
| 1. Moon | 6. Antarctica |
| 2. France | 7. Saturn |
| 3. Venus | 8. Venezuela |
| 4. Africa | 9. Transylvania |
| 5. New Jersey | 10. Peoria |

**CLOCK CLUB CLUES** (pages 8-9)

| | | | |
|---|---|---|---|
| 1. 9:00 | 4. 3:00 | 7. 1:00 | 10. 7:00 |
| 2. 2:00 | 5. 4:00 | 8. 5:00 | 11. 10:00 |
| 3. 12:00 | 6. 8:00 | 9. 6:00 | 12. 11:00 |

**LET'S GO FOR A SPIN** (page 10)

1. Wagon
2. Automobile
3. Train
4. Wheelbarrow
5. Trailer
6. Cart
7. Tricycle
8. Skateboard
9. Buggy
10. Plane
11. Bicycle
12. Mower
13. Motorcycle
14. Stroller
15. Tractor
16. Carriage

**WARM HOMECOMING** (page 11)

**CREATURE FEATURE** (pages 12-13)

1. B - cooing
2. C - squawking
3. A - soaring
4. C - crawling
5. A - bleating
6. B - hunting

**THIS ONE'S FOR THE BIRDS** (page 14)

3 5
6 2
1 4

**POETIC PATHWAY** (page 15)

I never saw a purple cow,
I never hope to see one;
But I can tell you, anyhow,
I'd rather see than be one!

## LUNCH LOGIC (page 18)

1. Rieko
2. Lee
3. Corinne
4. Kenny

## PICTURE CROSSWORD (page 19)

## SECRET SANDWICH (pages 20-21)

Spread a thick layer of peanut butter on two pieces of whole wheat toast. Peel a banana, slice it thinly, and spread the slices over the peanut butter. Put the sandwich halves together and serve it on a paper plate.

## ROW, ROW, ROW (page 22)

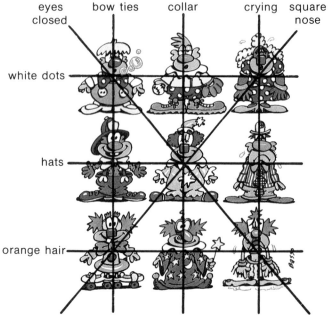

## PUZZLE PUZZLE (page 23)

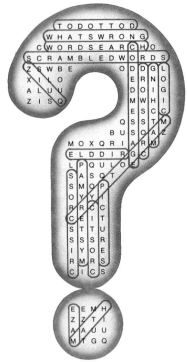

## BEACH BALL BONANZA (pages 24-25)

Ball A is exactly the same size as Sabrina's ball. Ball B is one-half the size, while ball C is twice as large.

## HARD TO PIN DOWN (page 26)

1. Safety pin
2. Bobby pin
3. Rolling pin
4. Straight pin
5. Clothespin
6. Bowling pin

## UNDERWATER MEMORIES (page 28)

1. There is one diver in the picture.
2. The deck chair is purple.
3. The diver had one tank.
4. The coral is orange.
5. An octopus is sitting on the wreck.
6. No, the sails are not unfurled.
7. The clam is holding a swimmer's flipper.
8. The lobster is reading a paper.
9. A dog is at the wheel of the ship.
10. Three portholes are visible on the sunken ship.

## MARY WHO? (page 28)

1 - E  Alice In Wonderland
2 - F  Hans Brinker
3 - I  Pippi Longstocking
4 - A  Tom Sawyer
5 - C  Winnie The Pooh
6 - J  Peter Pan
7 - H  Rebecca Of Sunnybrook Farm
8 - D  Robinson Crusoe
9 - G  Amelia Bedelia
10 - B  Anastasia Krupnik

## INSTANT PICTURE (page 29)

## CLEAN AS A SHELWIT (pages 30-31)

Cleaning my room is my favorite chore.
As soon as I'm finished, I clean it some more.
  I empty the wastebasket three times and then
  I plump up my pillow again and again.
I pick up my clothes every night, every day.
I vacuum and sweep till the rug wears away.
  I straighten my bookshelves first now and then later.
  The books are so straight, they can't get any straighter.
I polish my desk so it sparkles and shines.
My toys and my games stand like soldiers in lines.
  You won't find a cobweb, no smudge from a hand,
  I catch every dust speck before it can land.
My room is so tidy and perfectly neat.
If you had no plate, off the floor you could eat.
  But mom's still not happy, for I must confess . . .
  My room may be clean, but my closet's a mess!

## HOW LITTLE DO YOU KNOW? (page 32)

1. Little Bo Peep
2. Little Rock
3. Little Boy Blue
4. Chicken Little
5. Little John
6. Little Miss Muffet
7. The Little People
8. Little Bighorn, Montana
9. The Little Dipper (or the Little Bear)
10. Little America

## THE LONG AND THE SHORT OF IT (page 33)

Devon's path was the shortest. Gina's was the longest.

## MYSTERY MUNCHIES (pages 36-37)

A. Ice cream
B. Hamburgers
C. Popcorn
D. Pizza
E. Chocolate

## PICTURE MIXER (pages 38-39)

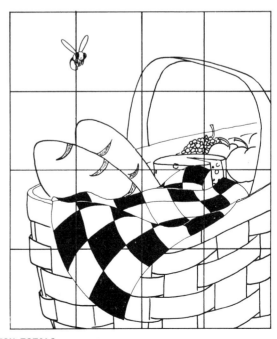

## TOY TOTALS (page 40)

We found 47 circles and 45 triangles in the picture.

**DOT MAGIC** (page 41)

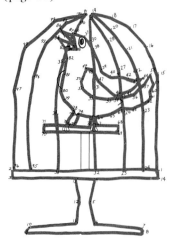

**CROSSWORD CROSSINGS** (pages 42-43)

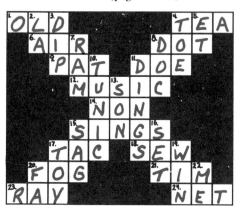

**TRIPLE TROUBLE** (page 44)
Trinka - B
Trevor - A
Trixie - C

**WHAT'S IN A WORD?** (page 45)
Here are some words we found in DINOSAUR. You
may have found others.

| | | | |
|---|---|---|---|
| aid | audio | raid | run |
| ad | din | rain | sad |
| adorn | drain | ran | said |
| an | in | rid | sand |
| and | is | rind | sir |
| as | no | road | son |
| arid | nor | rod | sound |
| arson | or | round | sun |
| around | our | ruin | undo |

**ZZZAP!** (page 46)

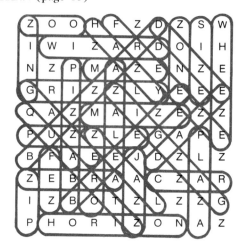

**Editor:** Jeffrey A. O'Hare • **Art Director:** Timothy J. Gillner
**Project Director:** Pamela Gallo • **Editorial Consultant:** Andrew Gutelle
**Design Consultant:** Bob Feldgus • **Senior Puzzler:** Donna Rehm Siple

**Puzzle Contributors**
Carsten Ahrens • Christopher Cardillo • Diane Cheffy • Jane C. Cross • Merri Lou Dobler
Anita C. Glockner • Kari L. Hickman • Cari Koerner • Virginia L. Kroll • Shirley Marshall • Thomas Mase
Darcie McNally • Clare Mishica • Lenora Pack • Linda Rose • Willow Jean Thompkins • Julie Woodman